Me and my teddy bea...

Words by Jack Winters, Music by J Fred Coots

Warner Chappell Music Ltd, London W1Y 3FA

Les bicyclettes de Belsize

Les Reed and Barry Mason

What Else Can I Play?
Violin
Grade One

	Piano part	Violin part
Daisy Bell	22	13
Edelweiss	6	3
A Groovy Kind Of Love	12	7
Heigh-ho	18	11
If	10	6
If You Knew Susie Like I Know Susie	20	12
Les Bicyclettes De Belsize	4	2
Mary's Boy Child	16	10
Me And My Teddy Bear	3	1
Moon River	26	16
Mountains Of Mourne	24	15
Oh, What A Beautiful Mornin'	9	5
Serenade	23	14
Soldiers' March	14	9
Three Little Fishies (Itty Bitty Poo)	13	8
We Wish You A Merry Christmas	8	4

© International Music Publications Ltd
First published in 1996 by International Music Publications Ltd
International Music Publications Ltd is a Faber Music company
Bloomsbury House 74–77 Great Russell Street London WC1B 3DA
Series Editor: Mark Mumford
Cover designed by Lydia Merrills-Ashcroft
Music arranged and processed by Barnes Music Engraving Ltd
Printed in England by Caligraving Ltd
All rights reserved

ISBN10: 0-571-53060-5
EAN13: 978-0-571-53060-1

To buy Faber Music publications or to find out about the full range of titles available,
please contact your local music retailer or Faber Music sales enquiries:

Faber Music Ltd, Burnt Mill, Elizabeth Way, Harlow, CM20 2HX England
Tel: +44(0)1279 82 89 82   Fax: +44(0)1279 82 89 83
sales@fabermusic.com   fabermusic.com

Introduction

In this *What Else Can I Play?* collection you'll find sixteen popular tunes that are both challenging and entertaining.

The pieces have been carefully selected and arranged to create ideal supplementary material for young violinists who are either working towards or have recently taken a Grade One violin examination.

As the student progresses through the volume, technical demands increase and new concepts are introduced which reflect the requirements of the major Examination Boards. Suggestions and guidelines on bowing, fingering, dynamics and tempo are given for each piece, together with technical tips and performance notes.

Pupils will experience a wide variety of music, ranging from folk and classical through to showtunes and popular songs, leading to a greater awareness of musical styles.

Whether it's for light relief from examination preparation, or to reinforce the understanding of new concepts, this collection will enthuse and encourage all young violin players.

6

Edelweiss

Words by Oscar Hammerstein II, Music by Richard Rodgers

Moderately ($\quarternote$ = 116)

We wish you a merry Christmas

Traditional

Oh, what a beautiful mornin'

Words by Oscar Hammerstein II, Music by Richard Rodgers

If

Words and Music by David Gates

A groovy kind of love

Words and Music by Toni Wine and Carole Bayer Sager

Three little fishies
(Itty bitty poo)

Words and Music by Saxie Dowell

Soldiers' march

Robert Schumann

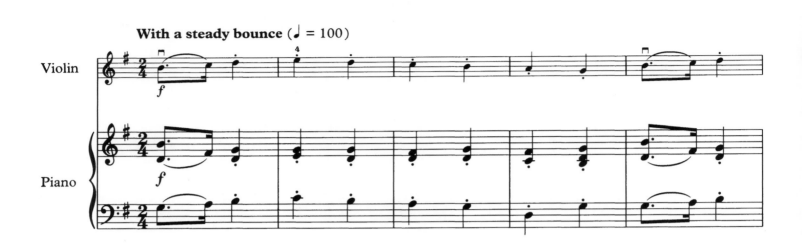

Mary's boy child

Words and Music by Jester Hairston

What Else Can I Play?
Violin
Grade One

Me and my teddy bear

Words by Jack Winters, Music by J Fred Coots

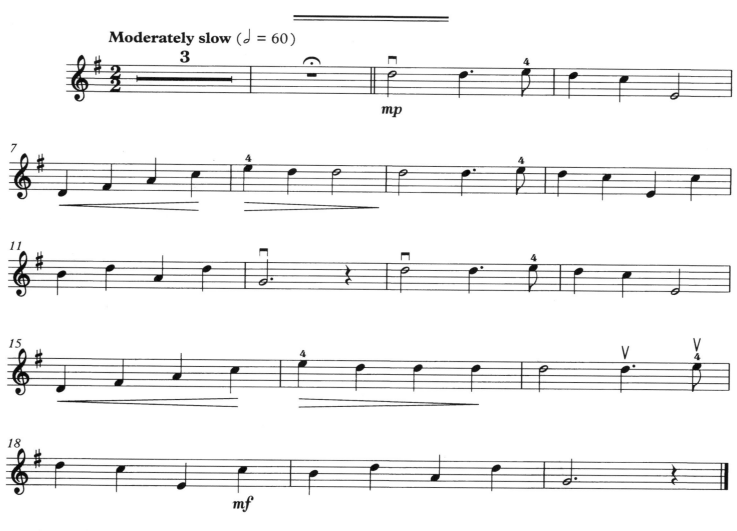

American singer Rosemary Clooney had success with this song in the early 1950s. Clooney's career included duets with Gene Autrey and Marlene Dietrich, but she is probably best remembered for her teamwork with Bing Crosby, with whom she appeared in the film *White Christmas* (1954).

This piece needs to sound cheerful, so use a lively bow stroke. Keep your fingers curved over the strings for the arpeggio patterns and make sure your second finger is ready to move quickly for the F sharps and C naturals.

Les bicyclettes de Belsize

Les Reed and Barry Mason

This song was a hit in 1968 for singer Englebert Humperdinck. He had previously performed under the less eccentric title of Gerry Dorsey but found greater success when relaunched with a name borrowed from the opera composer. The team that wrote this song also supplied Englebert's number one hit 'The Last Waltz' and provided Tom Jones with the dramatic 'Delilah'.

Try to make this piece flow. It is a waltz, with three beats in the bar and a slight emphasis on the first beat. For the pizzicato at the end, keep your bow hold and use your first finger to pluck. You may want to experiment for the best sound but you should find that plucking the string a short distance over the fingerboard is best.

Edelweiss

Words by Oscar Hammerstein II, Music by Richard Rodgers

The edelweiss is the national flower of Switzerland. This song is sung by Maria in the celebrated musical *The Sound Of Music*. Writers Rodgers and Hammerstein were responsible for some of the most famous musicals ever staged, including *South Pacific, The King And I, Carousel* and *Oklahoma!*

Try to play this piece as you would imagine singing it. Taking a breath whenever you reach a rest should help! Every new phrase begins with a down bow. At the end of bar 28 however, try saving the second half of your down bow for the beginning of bar 29. Watch out for the crescendo and diminuendo in the middle section – but don't overdo it!

We wish you a merry Christmas

Traditional

This West Country carol was often the concluding song to a visit by doorstep carol singers, indicating that they think they have earned 'some figgy pudding' and hinting, usually in good humour, that it could be the only way to get rid of them!

To help this tune sound jolly use a fast and lively bow stroke. Make sure the fingers of your left hand are on their tips, especially in bars 15 and 16, where the third finger hops across from the D to the A string.

Oh, what a beautiful mornin'

Words by Oscar Hammerstein II, Music by Richard Rodgers

This is one of several famous songs from the musical *Oklahoma!* Set in the American Midwest in pioneer days, this is the show's opening song which establishes the optimistic mood of Curly, the male lead, who goes on to beat his rival and win his gal!

Here is a good opportunity to practise your arpeggios. You might like to try giving each ascending phrase a slight crescendo. Retake the bow at the end of bar 12 – a down bow will give a positive start to the next phrase. Using only the upper half of the bow in the last four bars will help soften the tone.

If

Words and Music by David Gates

'If' is a hugely popular romantic ballad, written by David Gates of the pop group *Bread*. The song was first released in 1971.

This piece offers good practice for getting fourth fingers in tune. Try them where marked, they can sound more expressive than open strings. In bar 26 the B flat to E, first to fourth finger, will feel like a big stretch. Curve your fingers over the A string and don't let your wrist collapse. On the last note, slowly draw the bow close to the fingerboard to achieve the quiet ending.

A groovy kind of love

Words and Music by Toni Wine and Carole Bayer Sager

This song was written in the 1960s when the word 'groovy', meaning exciting or fashionable, was often used. In 1966 it was a hit record for UK group the *Mindbenders* and was also a big hit for Phil Collins in 1988.

The rhythm and bowing are quite straightforward. Don't forget the G sharps on the D string – be sure to stretch your third finger high enough and place the fourth finger close by – just a semitone away.

Three little fishies
(Itty bitty poo)

Words and Music by Saxie Dowell

This song might be mistaken for almost complete nonsense, subtitled as it is, 'Itty Bitty Poo'. A lot of people seem to remember the catchy refrain 'and they swam, and they swam right over the dam'.

It's a lively, cheerful tune which should be great fun to play. You need to be ready for the pizzicato notes – don't lose your bow hold! In bars 8 and 16 keep your third finger down to play G and play the G sharp like an A flat, with the fourth finger close to the third.

Soldiers' march

Robert Schumann

Robert Schumann (1810–1856) was one of the greatest melody writers of the nineteenth century. He composed in many forms, including symphonies and an opera, although it is his piano music, song-cycles and chamber works which are most frequently performed today.

Give this piece a strong marching rhythm and make the most of the contrasting dynamics and articulation. The last two notes need special emphasis to give the piece a strong ending.

Mary's boy child

Words and Music by Jester Hairston

This Christmas song was a big hit for singer Harry Belafonte, the man who helped to make the music of the West Indies so popular in the late 1950s. He charted three years running with this song and enjoyed a string of other hits, including 'Day O' ('The Banana Boat Song').

The piece is in A major so beware of the G sharps on the D string – make sure you stretch high enough! Play as smoothly as you can to help create the right mood. For the crescendos on the long notes at bars 10 and 18 start with a slow bow, at the point, and gradually speed up towards the heel.

Heigh-ho

Words by Larry Morey, Music by Frank E Churchill

This is perhaps the most famous song from the film *Snow White And The Seven Dwarfs* (1937), Walt Disney's first full-length animated film. The film took more than two years to make and was a huge success.

As with a lot of popular music dating from before 1950, this piece has an introductory verse before the well-known chorus, which starts at the end of bar 20. Play the piece as cheerfully as you can and count carefully, especially where there are dotted notes and tied notes.

If you knew Susie like I know Susie

Words and Music by Al Jolson, Joseph Meyer and Buddy de Sylva

This is a showtune from the 1920s, originally created for performer Al Jolson. Lyricist Buddy De Sylva collaborated with a number of composers, including Jerome Kern and George Gershwin. In later years he produced several successful musical films featuring child star Shirley Temple and in 1942 he was the co-founder of Capitol Records.

Make sure the playing is lively, with plenty of energy and swing. It will help if you slightly separate the crotchets. Look at bar 32 and you'll see that your left hand also has to be lively, with your first finger moving from F sharp to F natural and back in just three notes!

Daisy Bell

Words and Music by Harry Dacre

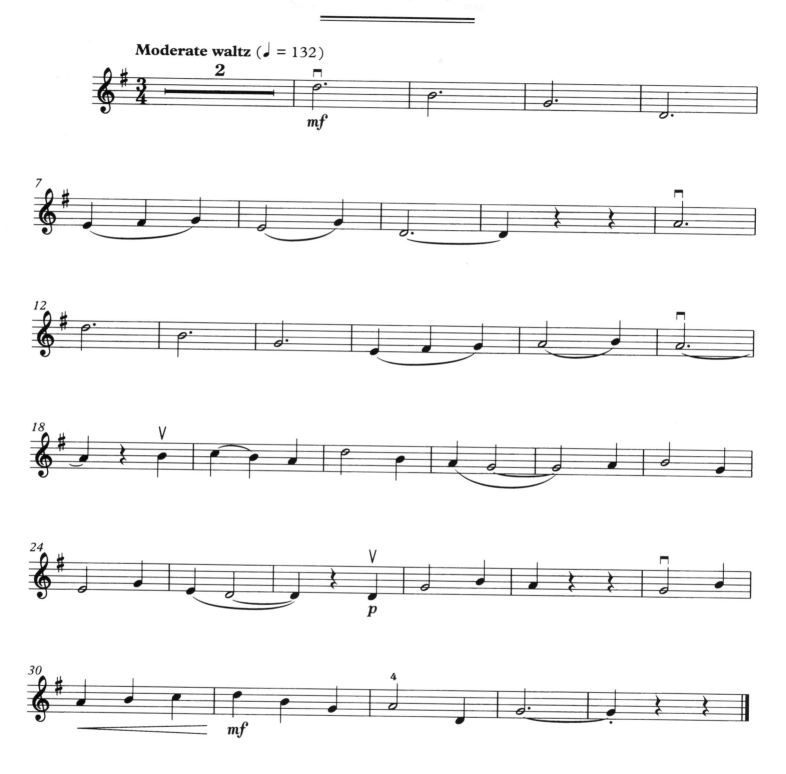

Also known as 'A Bicycle Built For Two' this cheeky song dates from the English music-hall of the 1890s where it was first popularly performed by the singer Katie Lawrence.

The piece has a cheerful, waltz feel, so enjoy it. Use plenty of bow and be careful to count the tied notes.

Serenade

Joseph Haydn

The word serenade is thought to derive from the Italian *sereno*, meaning calm, although a serenade is also considered to be music of the evening, *sera*.

Don't force the sound, let your bow arm move freely but use short lengths of bow for the separate quavers.

Mountains of Mourne

Traditional

This traditional Irish song enjoyed a popular revival around 1910 in a version credited to one William Percy French. It describes the yearnings of a man away from his home and his loved ones while 'digging for gold', perhaps working in the road gangs.

The tune is a light three-step with a lilting rhythm. You are helped by the fact that each four-bar phrase begins on the last beat of a bar. Pay special attention to the fingering in bar 23, where it will be helpful to move the first finger up behind the second finger to play the C natural.

Moon river

Words by Johnny Mercer, Music by Henry Mancini

'Moon River' comes from the film *Breakfast At Tiffany's* (1961) and in the year of its release won an Oscar for Best Song. During his lifetime Henry Mancini wrote the music to over one hundred films, including *The Pink Panther* (1964) and *The Great Race* (1965).

This piece should be calm and smooth, like a gently flowing river. The bowing may need some attention. Try bowing each note separately, and then re-introduce slurs when you feel you have the rhythm well under control.

Heigh-ho

Words by Larry Morey, Music by Frank E Churchill

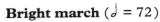

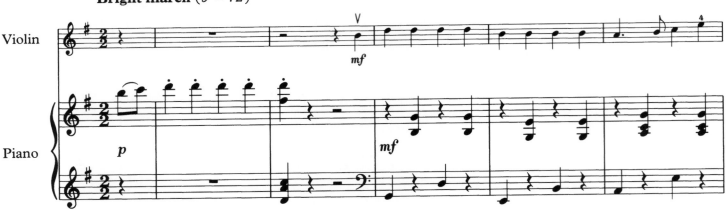

If you knew Susie like I know Susie

Words and Music by Al Jolson, Joseph Meyer and Buddy de Sylva

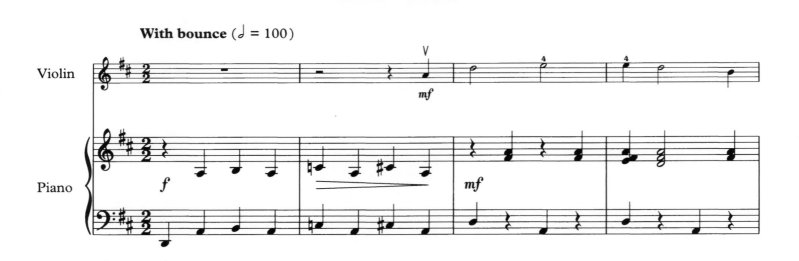

Daisy Bell

Words and Music by Harry Dacre

Serenade

Joseph Haydn

Mountains of Mourne

Traditional

Moon river

Words by Johnny Mercer, Music by Henry Mancini

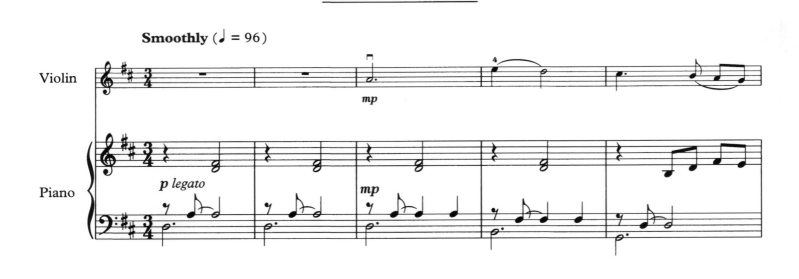

VIOLIN MUSIC FOR THE BEGINNER FROM FABER MUSIC

Mary Cohen's Superseries

Mary Cohen's *Superseries* has been hailed by string teachers worldwide as a breakthrough in violin teaching. Springing from Mary's unique pupil-centred approach to technical and musical learning, it encourages self-motivation and musicianship from the very first lesson.

The series covers work for the absolute beginner up to the advanced player.

'Be grateful to Cohen for her insight, imagination,
and the application of her ideas in teaching different violin skills.'
(*Music Teacher*)

Superstart NEW EDITION
*Basic skills and pieces
for beginners*

ISBN 0-571-52442-7 (with CD)
ISBN 0-571-52445-1 (piano acc.)

Superpieces
*Additional repertoire
for violin and piano*

BOOK 1 ISBN 0-571-51869-9 (complete)
BOOK 1 ISBN 0-571-51871-0 (violin part)
BOOK 2 ISBN 0-571-51870-2 (complete)
BOOK 2 ISBN 0-571-51872-9 (violin part)

Superstudies
*Original studies for the
young player*

BOOK 1 ISBN 0-571-51421-9
BOOK 2 ISBN 0-571-51450-2

Superduets
*Original and entertaining
duets for beginner violinists*

BOOK 1 ISBN 0-571-51889-3
BOOK 2 ISBN 0-571-51890-7

Scaley Monsters
*Scales without tears for
young violinists*

ISBN 0-571-51423-5

Space it!
*Easy well-known pieces
for violin*

ISBN 0-571-51806-0

FABER *ff* MUSIC